Introduction

"We cannot continue to lose"

How do you not see it as a moral imperative to get as many of those vehicles to theater as rapidly as you can?" Marine Commandant James Conway confronted Congress in 2007. He was frustrated with long delays in deploying mine resistant ambush protected (MRAP) after it had been repeatedly demonstrated the vehicles saved soldiers' lives.

Though the Unites Stated had encountered similar attacks during the Vietnam War and two decades later while patrolling between warring factions in Bosnia and Herzegovina as well as in Somalia, the military's collective memory seemed to falter when the United States and coalition forces launched the ground assault on Iraq on March 20, 2003. Utilizing conventional ground warfare tactics better suited for Northern Europe than the Middle Eastern nation of Iraq, the U.S. military failed to consider the enemy's proliferation of roadside bombs and improvised explosive devices (IEDs).

Not all field commanders waited for the bureaucratic process to find a solution to the IED threat. In June 2003, a Military Police commander in Iraq issued an urgent request for armored security vehicles (ASVs) to help protect military convoys and patrols. Three months later, at the behest of General John Abizaid, the Army created a small unit dedicated to defeating IEDs. About the same time, an "urgent universal need statement" for MRAPs began circulating the Pentagon. Part of it stated forcefully, "[We] cannot continue to lose…serious and grave casualties to IED and [motor vehicle accidents] at current rates when a commercial capability off the shelf exists…"

Replacing soft-skin vehicles with armored HMMWVs was thought to be the solution. In reality, the armored HMMWVs did provide occupants with protection from side-blasts, but the vehicles' flat-bottomed bellies made them especially vulnerable to under-vehicle attacks. The Government Accountability Office reported that, beginning in June 2003, "IED incidents targeting coalition forces began to escalate from 22 per month to over 600 a month…" a year later. Within three years, these incidents had reached 2,000 a month. Faced with a growing outcry from the military, political, and even the Nation's public, President George Bush made defeating the IED threat a top priority in March 2006.

V-Shaped Hulls

On May 21, 2006, Commanding General, Multi-National Force-West Richard C. Zilmer submitted a Staff Rapid Validation and Resourcing Request for 185 mine resistant ambush protected vehicles to the Joint Requirements Oversight Council (JROC). The approval cleared the way for the Pentagon to establish a joint Army / Marine MRAP acquisition program. They established three categories for the new vehicles:

Category I: Fire team-sized vehicles designed to hold up to seven occupants, including the driver, vehicle commander and gunner. These vehicles serve primarily as armored personnel carriers for fire teams and weapons carriers for medium and heavy machine guns. Reconnaissance units use Category I (CAT I) MRAPs to conduct mounted reconnaissance while employing long-range advance scout surveillance system (LRAS3). Generally, a CAT I MRAP vehicle was a 4x4 with a curb weight of no more than 30,000 pounds.

Category II: A CAT II vehicle is squad-sized, designed to hold 11 occupants, including the vehicle commander, driver and gunner. It is a multi-mission vehicle that provides a unit with protected transportation for convoy lead, ambulance or utility. Sapper and rifle squads use CAT II MRAPs for protected maneuver and movement when it is necessary to mass soldiers rapidly. CAT II MRAPs could be either 4x4 with a curb weight of no more than 30,000 pounds or 6x6 with a curb weight of not more than 38,000 pounds.

Category III: CAT III vehicles are equipped for mine and improvised explosive device clearance operations and explosive ordnance disposal. The vehicles transport no less than six personnel. CAT III vehicles are 6x6 with a curb weight of no more than 45,000 pounds.

Later, a fourth category, M-ATV, would be added, specifically to meet the demands of Operation Enduring Freedom—Afghanistan. M-ATVs were intended for small-unit combat operations in highly restricted rural, mountainous, and urban environments. M-ATVs carry up to five personnel (four plus a gunner).

The MaxxPro Family

The military's demand for MRAP vehicles mushroomed. In July 2007, U.S. Secretary of Defense Robert Gates requested $1.2 billion to fund 2,650 MRAP vehicles. Companies rushed to enter vehicles into the competition to become the United States' supplier of MRAPs. Force Protection, General Dynamics, BAE Systems, Armor Holdings, and Oshkosh had all been busy developing vehicles.

Even though Navistar or its subsidiary, International Military Government LLC (IMG), didn't have expertise in armored vehicles, it did know trucks. In addition to being one of America's largest producers of civilian commercial trucks and mid-range Diesel engines, it had experience producing trucks for the Afghan National Army and the U.S. Government. Navistar believed, if they could find the right partner, they could build an entrant for the MRAP race based around the IMG's WorkStar 7000 truck chassis.

As early as March 2005, the firm contracted with Armour Technology Systems Ltd (ATS). Formed in 2004, the small South African firm had the design rights to several mine-resistant vehicles in service with the South African military, particularly the Oryx 4x4 and blast-resistant SAMIL armored cabs for the South African Army's trucks.

About the same time, Navistar established a relationship with Plasan Sasa. The Israeli firm had designed and was manufacturing up-armoring kits for the U.S. Marine Corps' fleet of MTVR trucks. Navistar decided they found the right partner to move ahead with an MRAP design. In January 2007, they cancelled their agreement with ATS and began a partnership between IMG and Plasan Sasa.

IMG knew its WorkStar 7000 chassis had the load capacity to carry the weight of an armored crew compartment. Working with Plasan, IMG's final design positioned a V-shaped compartment on top of the chassis. The armor was bolted together, rather than welded

as on other MRAPs. This plan maxi─── ───mmonality by using the compartment's shar─── ───asts around the crew area. Furthermore─── ───mponents coupled with predic─── ───hat the IMG/Plasan en─── ───ucible in large nu───

Followi─── ───uations of four IMG─── ───g Ground in March 2007, a─── ───ate Initial Production (LRIP) ora─── ───00 Category I MRAPs. This was followed─── ─── a follow-up order for 16 Category II MRAP Join─── ───nance Disposal (EOD) Rapid Response Vehicle (JE─── ───quad vehicles.

IMG's initial design was for a Category I vehicle simply called the International MaxxPro ("Maximum Protection"). The military labeled the Cat I MRAP the M1224.

Powered by Navistar's MaxxForce D8.7 I-6 turbo inter-cooled, direct electronic injection engine coupled with a fully automatic Allison 3000 transmission, the 4x4 could reach a top speed of 72 mph while carrying a crew of two plus four seated soldiers and one gunner in the roof-mounted turret.

IMG's Category II version produced to fill the 2007 order for 16 JERRV vehicles was referred to as the MaxxPro XL. Longer than the base vehicle by 24 inches (though built on the same chassis), the XL was capable of carrying up to 10 soldiers. Three bullet-resistant windows on each side of the crew compartment quickly identified the MaxxPro as an XL model

By July 2007, the MaxxPro was the military's primary MRAP vehicle. IMG held 35% of all orders issued under the initial MRAP program.

At that time, however, the insurgents increasingly attacked with Explosively-Formed Penetrators (EFPs)—a type of standoff IED that employed a shaped charge against the sides of vehicles. The Marines Corps System Command (who, at this time were responsible for all MRAP procurement) responded by issuing an MRAP II Enhanced Vehicle Competition in July 2007. But, to immediately address the EFP threat with some similar level of protection for MRAP vehicles already in service, the Marines Corps System Command created the MRAP Expedient Armor Program (MEAP).

IMG responded to the call by designing an up-armor kit that could be attached to existing MaxxPros. Under the MRAP II program, a total of 550 MEAP-ready MaxxPro vehicles were accepted: 50 retrofitted with boss-style attachments and 500 vehicles made MEAP-ready at IMG. They are often referred to as MaxxPro MEAP Protected vehicles or M1224A1s.

In the field, however, the additional 10,000 lbs of EFP armor proved to be too much weight for the standard WorkForce 7000 chassis. An April 2008 firm-fixed-priced contract modification of $261.3 million covered several engineering changes, additional armor protection, and ambulance kits. That June, IMG revealed an upgraded vehicle capable of carrying the increased EFP protection. Labeled the MaxxPro Plus or the M1234, the new Category I vehicle was designed to accept the Frag Kit 6 appliqué armor package. Without EFP armor, the Plus weighed about 5,000 pounds more than the base model MaxxPro. To carry the extra weight, IMG provided the chassis with load-carrying dual rear wheels and a 375-horsepower D9.3 I-6 MaxxForce engine.

IMG also created an ambulance version on the same platform, the MaxxPro Plus Ambulance. The military gave it the nomenclature M1234A1.

Though ideally suited for the relatively flat terrain of Iraq, Afghanistan's rugged terrain severely limited the MaxxPro vehicle's mobility. Fearing a loss of sales, Navistar Defense (as it was now known) returned to the drawing board to produce a vehicle that could successfully meet the challenges of Afghanistan. Within a month of announcing the receipt of a contract worth more than $752 million to produce a lighter, smaller variant of the MaxxPro family of vehicles, Navistar Defense began production of 822 MaxxPro Dash vehicles at its West Point, Mississippi, plant in October 2008.

Christened the M1235, the MaxxPro Dash was 5,000 lbs lighter and 16 inches shorter than the earlier MaxxPros. It also boasted a 145" wheelbase that enabled it to make a tight, 54-foot turn radius. The 570 cu. in. MaxxForce D9.3 I-6 engine— the same found in the Plus—could propel the 34,000-pound 4x4 to a top speed of 67mph. The similarity to the earlier MaxxPros ended there, though. The Dash was built to accept full A-Kit EFP armor—a different package than used on the MaxxPro Plus .

Despite a second order for 400 additional Dash vehicles in December 2008, complaints were coming in from soldiers in Afghanistan that the Dash was not satisfactorily navigating the rugged terrain. Navistar responded by subcontracting with Hendrickson Truck Suspension Systems to provide an independent suspension that could be incorporated into the current design as well as adapted to earlier MaxxPro models.

When the Marine Corps ordered 1,050 MaxxPro Dash vehicles with a contract award in February 2009, Navistar incorporated Henrickson's DXM independent suspensions. Designated the M1235A1 but also called the MaxxPro Dash DXM or Dash ISS, the upgraded vehicles featured engineered sub-frames that coupled sway bars, coil springs, and shocks with Axle Tech's 5000 series Independent Suspension Axle System (ISAS). The new undercarriage enabled improved rough terrain mobility through better control and greater wheel travel. Other improvements to the original Dash design included door and insulation upgrades, as well as the addition of an inclinometer to act as a level and measure side slope during vehicle operation.

Beginning with the 2009 order, Navistar initiated a program to retrofit the entire MaxxPro fleet with the new independent suspension. Work began, in country, with retrofitting 1,222 Dash vehicles with the DXM improved suspension. Navistar called this program the "Rolling Chassis Solution." The program allows the armored capsule to be transferred from the old chassis to the new independent suspension-equipped chassis. In this way, the entire fleet will be standardized with the DXM suspension, MaxxForce 9.3 engine, 570-amp alternator, and driveline.

In May 2011, Navistar received an order for 250 Dash DXM with an ambulance kit. Designated the M1235A2, the ambulance's most attractive feature was the automatic litter assist system. The M1235A2 was intended to replace the original, solid-axle MaxxPro

The MaxxPro MRAP Family

Model	Also known as	Identifiers
M1224	MaxxPro Base	Vertical slat grille, two windows on the crew cabin, single rear tires.
MaxxPro XL	Cat II MaxxPro	Vertical slat grille, three windows on the crew cabin, single rear tires.
M1224A1	MaxxPro MEAP	Vertical slat grille, two windows on the side, EFP armor plates, single rear wheels.
M1234	MaxxPro Plus	Horizontal slat grille, two windows, dual rear wheels (may or may not be equipped with EFP armor).
M1234A1	MaxxPro Plus Ambulance	Same attributes as M1234. Externally identifiable by Red Cross markings.
M1235	MaxxPro Dash	Horizontal slat grille, single rear wheels, shorter crew compartment than on the M1234 best seen by shape of profile, V-shaped hull visible where it meets the chassis.
M1235A1	MaxxPro Dash DXM or ISS	Same attributes of the M1235 except: 6" taller, downward curve on the bottom of front suspension, coiled springs, CTIS fitted to wheels.
M1235A2	MaxxPro Dash DXM Ambulance	Same attributes of the M1235A1. Externally identifiable by Red Cross markings.
M1235A3	MaxxPro DXM MSU	Same attributes of the M1235A1 with the addition of welded external seams.
M1249	MRV	6x6, 30-ton boom recovery body with a crane mounted on the rear side of the chassis.
M1249-PVK	MRV-PVK	Same attributes as M1249 plus DXM independent suspension fitted to the front wheels, CTIS fitted to remaining wheels.

Ambulance, the M1234A1. The M1234A1 failed to fully meet objective requirements for safe and easily accessible litter loading. Because the back of the ambulance was elevated and required a ladder to enter the crew compartment, four soldiers had to lift and load a casualty—a labor and time-intensive process. However, the M1235A2 Dash ambulance was coming up short—so short, in fact, the smaller crew compartment (nearly 18" shorter than on the M1234A1) could not safely accommodate patients taller than 5'11.". Furthermore, the Dash ambulance interior was not large enough to accommodate the required medical equipment to treat patients. A solution had to be found.

As part of the ongoing process to upgrade the entire fleet of MaxxPros, Navistar discovered a solution while upgrading the M1234A1s. By retrofitting compartments on the long wheelbase vehicles with the litter assist system used on the Dash ambulances, the litter loading / unloading time was reduced to under 20 seconds and required only two people to accomplish. Because the M1234A1 crew compartment was about 18 inches longer than on the Dash, patients taller than 6'3" (the Army's standard) could be comfortably accommodated. And finally, the rear dual-wheeled design easily carries the increased payload of the ambulance kit. The retrofitted ambulances have been labeled "MaxxPro LWB Ambulance."

Around the same time, Navistar introduced the MaxxPro MRAP Recovery Vehicle (MRV). Providing the same ballistic protection as the MaxxPro MRAP, the 6x6 wrecker is capable of recovering all Category I and II MRAP vehicles as well as all Stryker variants under combat conditions. It is fitted with a 30-ton boom recovery body with a crane mounted on the rear side of the chassis. In November 2010, Marine Corps Systems Command ordered 250 MRVs. The military designation for the MRV is M1249. An additional order for 140 MRVs with rocket propelled grenade (RPG) defeating nets soon followed.

Though acquired in relatively large numbers, the M1249s were criticized for their lack of cross-country mobility when towing damaged MRAPs in Afghanistan. This led to Navistar's 2012 introduction of an upgrade kit: MaxxPro Recover Vehicle-PVK. The PVK upgrade included a 20% increase in engine power, DXM independent suspension fitted to the front wheels, central tire inflation system, and a six channel, anti-lock braking system.

By 2013, with the war in Iraq concluded and the war in Afghanistan winding down, the Joint Program Office Mine Resistant Ambush Protected-Operation Enduring Freedom (JPO MRAP-OEF) continued to refine its efforts to protect soldiers with lessons learned after more than a decade at war. The Office authorized more than 1,000 M1235A1 MaxxPro Dash DXMs already in Afghanistan to undergo the MaxxPro Survivability Upgrade (MSU). Focusing on blast mitigation, the upgrades were purported to increase survivability by 75% through four times the blast protection. The upgraded vehicles were designated M1235A3s. This was the last significant change made to the entire family of MaxxPro MRAPs.

After only eight years, total production of MaxxPro MRAPs stood at around 8,779 vehicles—nearly one third of the total number of MRAPs fielded by the United States in Iraq and Afghanistan. And after only eight years, the U.S. military was already in the process of decommissioning its vast fleet of MaxxPro's. As the U.S. withdrew troops from Afghanistan, some vehicles returned to the United States, some were put into long-term storage on foreign soil, many were given to coalition forces, while others were simply destroyed—1,000 in 2014.

MaxxPros remain in service with the military forces of Albania, Croatia, Estonia, Greece, Hungary, Jordan, Pakistan, Poland, Romania, Slovakia, and the Republic of Korea. Pakistan and the United Arab Emirates have requested more than 4,700 new or refurbished MaxxPros, guaranteeing the vehicle will continue in operations for many more years. With much of the information surrounding these vehicles remains classified, historians, veterans, and scholars have begun the task of unraveling the details about this family of vehicles that had protected the U.S. military on two violent war fronts during the first decade and a half of the 21st Century.

MaxxPro MRAP

A VISUAL HISTORY OF THE MAXXPRO MINE RESISTANT AMBUSH PROTECTED VEHICLES

by John Adams-Graf with David Doyle

Published by
Ampersand Group, Inc.
A HobbyLink Japan company
235 NE 6th Ave., Suite B
Delray Beach, FL 33483-5543
561-266-9686 • 561-266-9786 Fax
www.ampersandpubco.com • www.hlj.com

Acknowledgements:
Many of the images used in this book were taken by the Soldiers, Airmen, Sailors, or Marines who had been tasked to operating in combat conditions. Truly, without their penchant for fine photography under duress, this book would not have been possible. Additionally, the generous assistance of John Lewis, Sgt. Michael MacLeod, Arthur Macon, and Nathan Machula helped to tell the story of the MaxxPro family of vehicles.

All unattributed photos are copyright of the authors.

Sources:
*Lamb, Christopher J., Mathew J. Schmidt and Berit G. Fitzsimmons,
MRAPS, Irregular Warfare, and Pentagon Reform,
(Washington, DC: National Defense University Press, 2009).*

*TC 7-31 Mine Resistant Ambush Protected (MRAP) Family of Vehicles
Driver Training (US Army: February 2011)*

*No. 08-30 MRAP Vehicles Handbook,
(U.S. Army Combined Arms Center: September 2008)*

*No. 11-11 MRAP and M-ATV Vehicles Handbook, Vol. II
(U.S. Army Combined Arms Center: February 2011)*

*PBC-07-1291 Customs Parts Catalog, IMPV Category I, Revision E
(International Military Government, LLC: Sept. 27, 2007)*

*PBC-07-1291 Customs Parts Catalog, IMPV Category II,
(International Military Government, LLC, Sept. 27, 2007)*

*TM 9-2355-106-10 Operator Manual Commercial Off-the-Shelf (COTS)
for International Mine Resistant Vehicle (US Army: Sept. 11, 2007)*

*TM-9-2355-324-24P1 Repair Parts and Special Tools List (RPSTL)
Manual Commercial Off-the-Shelf (COTS) for MaxxPro Dash Mine Resistant
Ambush Protected (MRAP) Vehicle, Category I (US Army: June 2010)*

Cover: From its introduction in 2007, the Navistar MaxxPro evolved to meet the demands of U.S. military personnel in defeating the effects of improvised explosive devices on vehicles in the theaters of operation in Iraq in Afghanistan. By 2015, nearly 9,000 MaxxPro MRAP variants had been in service with 16 nations in addition to the United States. (U.S. Air Force, Tech. Sgt. Craig Lifton)

Rear cover: Iraqi security forces receive a shipment of 30 MaxxPro mine-resistant, ambush-protected (MRAP) vehicles with mine-roller attachments at Camp Taji, Iraq, on 13 July 2015. The MRAPs are part of the Iraq Train and Equip Fund meant to assist in the fight against the Islamic State of Iraq and the Levant. The 310th Advise and Assist Team, 13th Sustainment Command (Expeditionary) and the 1st Theater Sustainment Command supervised the delivery of the vehicles in support of Combined Joint Task Force—Operation Inherent Resolve. (U.S. Army photo by Staff Sgt. Brian McDermott)

Title page: Multi Integrated Laser Engagement System (MILES) specialists inventory MaxxPro Mine-Resistant, Ambush Protected Vehicles during a mission rehearsal exercise (MRE) at the Joint Multinational Readiness Center in Hohenfels, Germany, 4 August 2015. Georgian soldiers conduct the MRE alongside U.S. Marine Corps mentors before deploying to Afghanistan in order to hone the skills necessary to operate alongside International Security Assistance Force partner forces in a counterinsurgency environment. (U.S. Army photo by Spc. Tyler Kingsbury)

Table of Contents

A MaxxPro manned by Marines assigned to Combat Logistics Battalion 3's Motor Transportation Company powers out of a deep, simulated wadi during a simulated convoy test run through the Combat Vehicle Operators Training - Afghan Course, using multiple vehicles at Camp Bastion, Islamic Republic of Afghanistan, 29 March 2009. (Lance Cpl. Ronald Stauffer)

M1224

Designed as a Category II vehicle to fill an order for 16 Joint Explosive Ordnance Disposal Rapid Response Vehicles (JERRVs), the MaxxPro XL was longer than the base vehicle—though built on the same chassis. The three louvered, bullet-resistant windows and four gun ports on each side quickly identify the vehicle. (U.S. Army)

Based on the Workstar Model 7000 truck chassis, the base model Category I M1024 is easily identified by the vertical armored radiator grille slats, single air vents on each side of the hood, and single tires on the rear axle. (Navistar)

M1224 MaxxPro Specifications

Type	Category I MRAP
Length	254 inches
Width	102 inches
Height	120 inches
Minimum ground clearance	10.9 inches
GVWR	43,500 lbs.
Kit weight	4,500 lbs.
Engine	MaxxForce D8.7 Diesel
Horsepower	330 @ 2,100 rpm
Maximum speed	69.2 mph
Minimum turning distance (curb to curb)	62 feet
Maximum slope	Up to 60%
Center of gravity (GVW vertical)	59.4 inches

STUDENT DRIVER

Though reported to have a ground clearance of 14 inches, drivers soon discovered that clearance at the differential was only 11 inches. As a result, most of the early M1224s were relegated to road duty with very limited off-road driving. (U.S. Army, Staff Sgt. Anna Rutherford)

The standard M1224 crew configuration called for a driver and navigator. In addition, the MaxxPro can carry up to six passengers and a gunner. (U.S. Army, Sgt. Mark B. Matthews)

Behind the vertical slats, a turbo inter-cooled MaxxForce 8.7D I-6-Diesel, 8.7-liter engine produces up to 330 horsepower at 2,100 rpm. The headlights mounted on the hood are sealed halogen beam units. Two blackout marker lights with amber lenses are located near the each end of the bumper. A blackout light and a small infrared lamp are positioned on the left side of the left towing eye. (David Doyle)

All armor is fixed in place. Each door opens with a single lever. Once inside, however, the operator can employ a combat latch that locks the door from outside entrance. The gun port located just below the window can be opened and sealed from inside the vehicle without the use of tools. (David Doyle)

The armored window covers are bolted on the vehicle, and the ballistic transparent windows do not open. Ventilation is provided by the HVAC/LSS (Heating Ventilation & Air-Conditioning/Life Support Systems). (David Doyle)

There are four external stowage boxes located on the vehicle. Two are located just in front of the rear wheels behind the cab doors and two are located just behind the rear wheels. The perforated panel provides protected ventilation for the air conditioner condenser. The fire suppression unit for the fuel tank is located on the left side behind the fans of the air conditioner. (David Doyle)

A 70-gallon fuel tank is located below the left door. A small door on the upper left allows access to add Diesel or JP8 fuel. Two steps allow access to the driver's compartment. (David Doyle)

The power steering assembly is attached to a Pitman arm and steering gear drag, visible near the tire in this view of the underside of the left front of the vehicle. (David Doyle)

Looking behind the left side of the front bumper, you can see the wiring harness to the light bumper lights and headlight as well as the plumbing for the Gladhand connector. (David Doyle)

With a view toward the right rear wheel, the rear drive-shaft is seen connected to the rear differential. The exhaust runs just above it. (David Doyle)

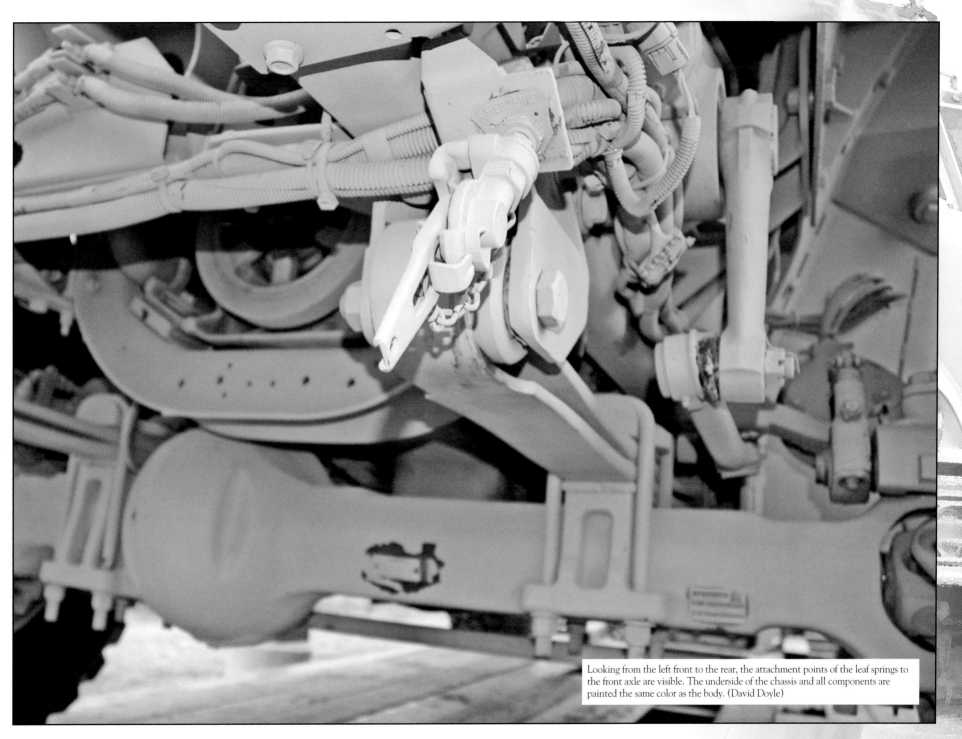

Looking from the left front to the rear, the attachment points of the leaf springs to the front axle are visible. The underside of the chassis and all components are painted the same color as the body. (David Doyle)

Armor plate is fitted on either side of the transfer case. Armor also protects the engine compartment, fitted lower than the blast deflector. (David Doyle)

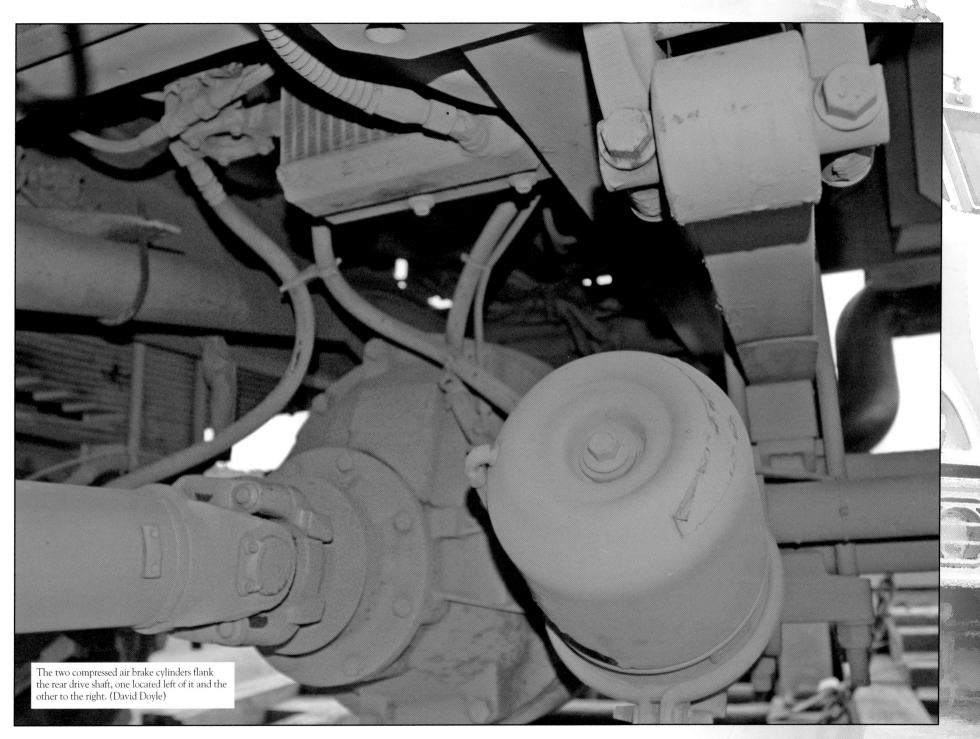

The two compressed air brake cylinders flank the rear drive shaft, one located left of it and the other to the right. (David Doyle)

The rear drive (or "propeller") shaft connects to the transfer case with universal joints held in a yoke. The shaft shield has started to lose paint, revealing the black rubber of which it is made. (David Doyle)

The rear semi-elliptical leaf springs are secured to the axle by two U-shaped bolts and a rubber seat. An auxiliary rubber spring above the rubber seat and attached to a chassis-mounted bracket adds additional cushioning. (David Doyle)

Though very flexible, the entire spring assembly (including the mounting brackets and the rubber bushings) is painted. The non-metallic conduit feeding the two forward Gladhand connectors is covered with black nylon tubing. (David Doyle)

The M1224 runs on Michelin 395/85R20 tires mounted on Hutchinson Runflat rims. Variable Function Inserts (VFI) increase protection and survivability from mine blasts. Ten studs and nuts hold the entire wheel assembly to the hub. The fill valve is visible inside the ring of hub nuts. (David Doyle)

A complete fire suppression system (FSS) protects the tires, fuel tank, cabin, and engine. Suppression for the first two is manually initiated, while the latter work automatically or manually. (David Doyle)

Left: The cabin, engine, tires, body, and fuel tank are protected with the fire suppression systems. Only the cabin and engine systems are automatic. All these systems can be operated manually by the driver of the vehicle in case of malfunction in automatic systems. The system includes: heat detector for the engine, heat detector for the interior, dispersion system, fire suppression units, and dispersion nozzles (seen here). **Right:** A look behind the right front tire reveals weld spots and bolt-on armor techniques. (David Doyle, both)

The fuel/water separator assembly is located above the axle on the right front side of the vehicle. Apparently, this particular filter was in place before final painting of the vehicle as overspray and shadow are visible. The shock absorber is visible just behind the filter. Shock absorbers may have a thin film of oil on the outer surface known as "misting" due to normal operating conditions. (David Doyle)

Whereas both door mirrors are controlled from inside the cabin, the fender-mounted mirrors are manually adjusted. The vehicle has a front-mounted, deployable self-recovery winch system that is used for self-recovery operations. (David Doyle)

The wiring harness and bracket for the right bumper lighting are painted in the overall sand color. (David Doyle)

Passenger access to the vehicle is through the rear ramp. The MaxxPro vehicles were the only vehicles in the line of U.S.-deployed MRAPs to have a hydraulically controlled rear door. Descent of the M1224's door takes between 17 and 19 seconds. The descent speed was improved on the MaxxPro Plus, and eventually, all MaxxPro vehicles were upgraded with a system (first deployed on the M1235 MaxxPro Dash) that had a 6-second ramp speed, up or down. A panel inside and above the door contains a toggle switch to supply hydraulic power to operate the ramp. There are also controls in the driver's area for the operation of the ramp. The ramp can also be raised manually in an emergency. Five amber clearance lights are located on a bar above the ramp. (David Doyle)

There are two additional stowage compartments on the MaxxPro located on both left and right sides near the rear wheels (left rear pictured). Items for each stowage unit are determined by local load plans. (David Doyle)

There are four blackout marker lights, two on the front bumper and two on the rear. A white backup light is next to the blackout marker light. (David Doyle)

Two brackets on the rear of the vehicle hold two 5-gallon water or fuel cans each. They are mounted on either side of the rear door/ramp exit. The words "FUEL" or "WATER" are molded into each can for identification. Ladder brackets are located on the rear corners of the vehicle, above and below the jerry can brackets. (David Doyle)

The muffler assembly is retained by two straps and exhausts to the left rear of the vehicle. The exhaust pipe, below the left rear blackout light, is shielded by a sheet metal protector. (David Doyle)

The rear bracket for the lower step on the right side of the vehicle. (David Doyle)

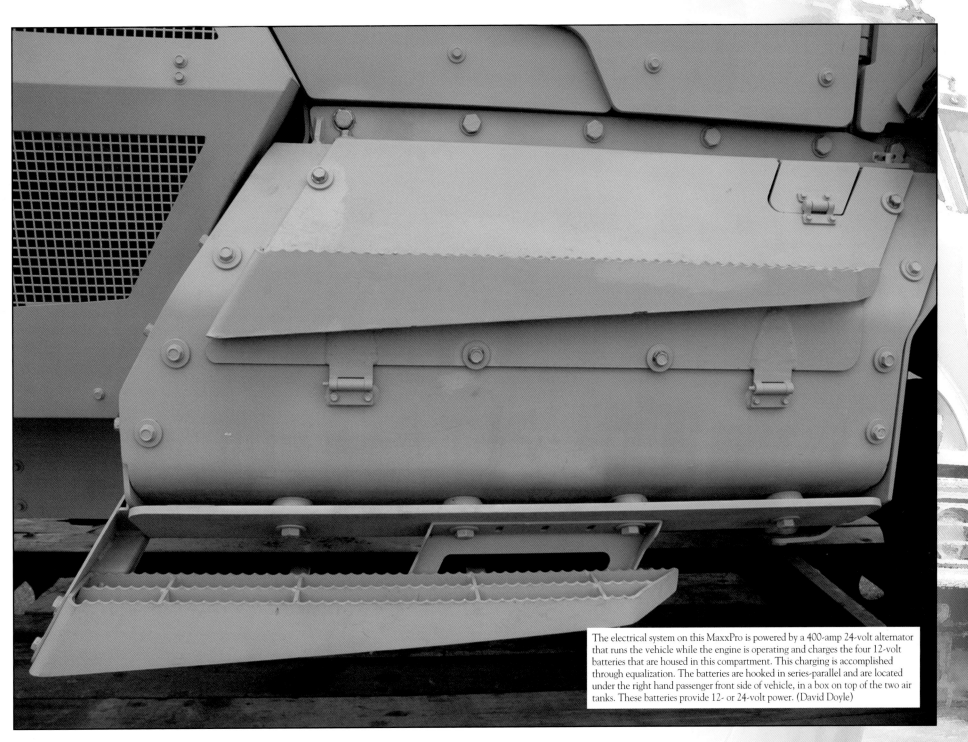

The electrical system on this MaxxPro is powered by a 400-amp 24-volt alternator that runs the vehicle while the engine is operating and charges the four 12-volt batteries that are housed in this compartment. This charging is accomplished through equalization. The batteries are hooked in series-parallel and are located under the right hand passenger front side of vehicle, in a box on top of the two air tanks. These batteries provide 12- or 24-volt power. (David Doyle)

A 110-volt power inverter box is located inside the right front stowage box is for assisted powering with auxiliary equipment. The inverter box is located next to the NATO slave receptacle used to start a disabled vehicle. The air conditioning radiator is behind the grill in front of the stowage box. (David Doyle)

Handles on the side of the vehicle provide an area for equipment stowage. The vertical handle next to the door is to assist in entrance/exit. The loop above the stowage box is one of two on the side of the vehicle for tie-down. A lifting hook is visible at the top of the vehicle. (David Doyle)

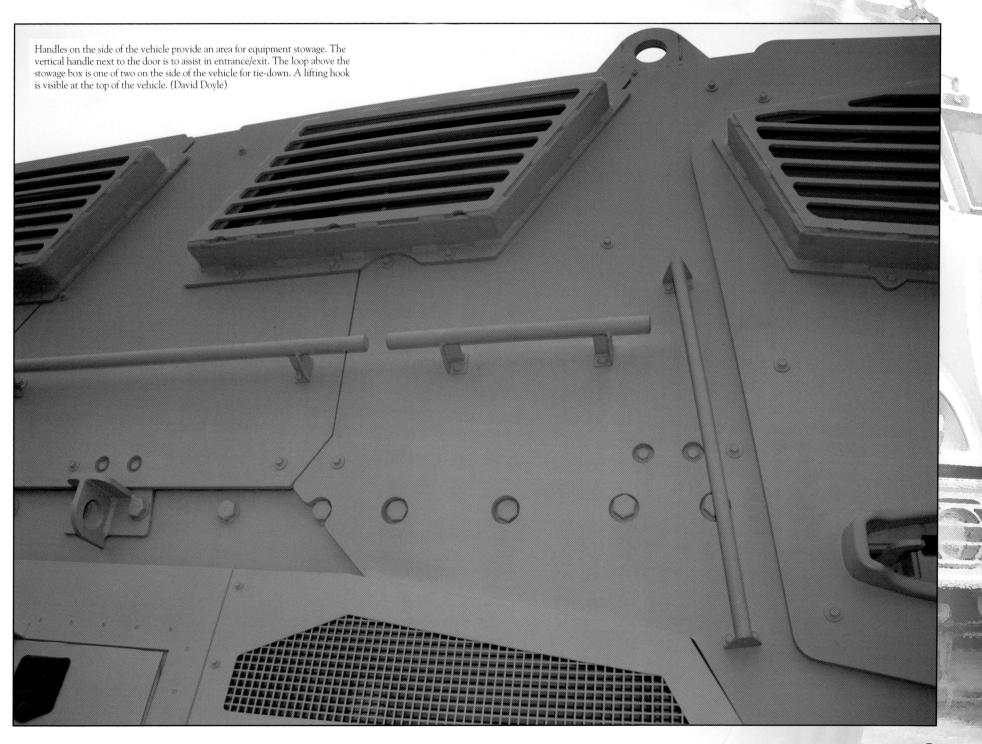

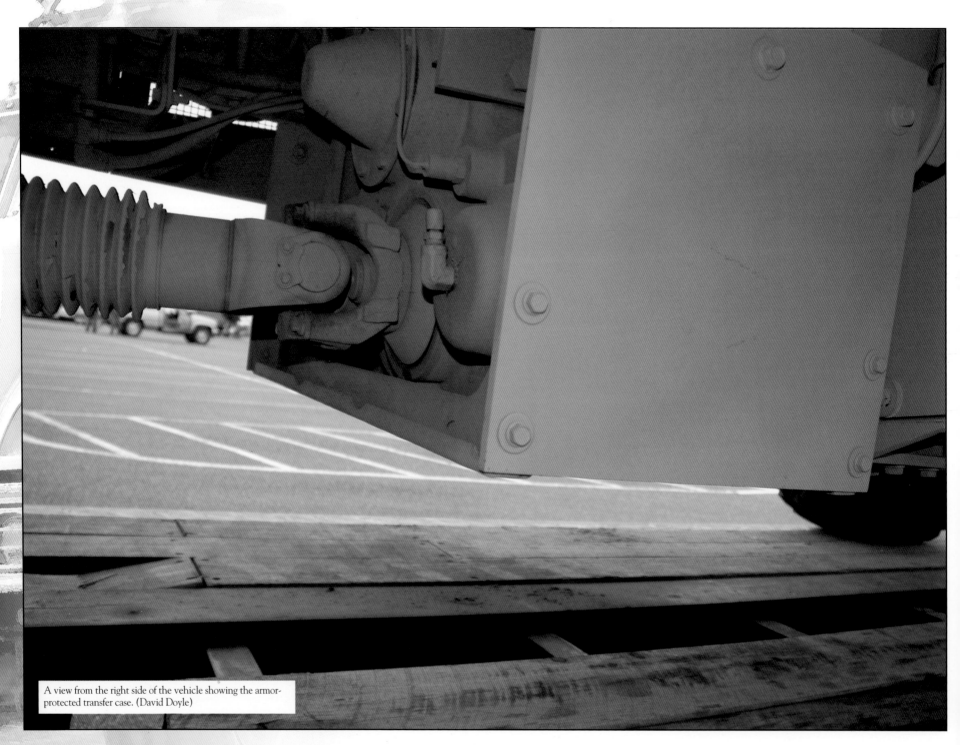

A view from the right side of the vehicle showing the armor-protected transfer case. (David Doyle)

There are no locks on the outside of either door. A common field expedient is to padlock a chain running through the handle and the side bar. The mirror is folded in the transport position in this photo. (David Doyle)

Army-contracted civilian longshoremen loading M1224s onto a ship in Charleston, S.C., in March 2008. These vehicles were shipped to Central Command. The U.S. Marine Corps had ordered 2,971 MaxxPros to be delivered by April of that year. Navistar International Corporation shipped more than 400 of the vehicles within 165 days of its first contract award on May 31, 2007. (USMC, Master Sgt. Kevin Young)

The first MaxxPro M1224 shipments arrived at Camp Liberty in western Baghdad and were being fielded to units who operated in areas with the highest threat levels. Each of these vehicles was equipped with a turret known as the Objective Gunner Protection Kit (O-GPK). (U.S. Army, Sgt. Mark B. Matthews)

A Terex TFC 45 reach stacker operated by the 2nd Battalion, 402nd Army Field Support Brigade, RPAT Yard at Joint Base Balad, Iraq simplified the task of moving the 21-ton MaxxPros. (U.S. Army, Galen Putnam)

Though most MRAPs were delivered to theaters of operation by ship, they were designed to be transported by the C-17 Globemaster III or C-5 Galaxy/Super Galaxy. This M1124 is boarding an civilian-operated Antonov An-124 Ruslan heavy transport, the Russian equivalent of the C-5 Galaxy. (U.S. Army, Spc. Karen L. Kozub)

Plasan supplied a composite-based applied armor solution that bolted onto the MaxxPro, providing complete driver and crew cabin protection. (U.S. Army, 1st Lt. Christian Venhuizen)

The MaxxPro's 55-59' turning radius was achieved though a hydraulically assisted recirculating ball system. Here, soldiers from B Battery, 2nd Battalion, 300th Field Artillery, 115th Fires Brigade try to maneuver their MaxxPro out of a sand pit in an obstacle course. (U.S. Army, 1st Lt. Christian Venhuizen)

Soldiers from the 501st Military Police Company began a driving road test in one of the five Mine Resistant Ambush Protected vehicles used during pre-deployment training at the Grafenwoehr Training Area. (U.S. Army, Sgt. Jason Stadel)

The rear ramp has one external step (seen at the top of the door) and four internal steps. Plagued by a slow lowering/raising time, Navistar quickly made changes for faster deployment. Regardless, military officials have commented that the steps are points of obstruction for soldiers using them under duress. (ASA-Dix Public Affairs, Ryan Morton)

Though the M1224 can achieve up speed up to 72 mph, the Center for Army Lessons Learned (CALL) advised the vehicle should not be operated at more than 15 mph on rough secondary roads or mild, off-road terrain or more than 10 mph on more severe terrain to avoid possible injury to crew or passengers and damage to the vehicle's suspension and drive train. CALL also determined that sustained operation on highways at over 55 mph could result in tire failure. (U.S. Army, Sgt. David Bruce)

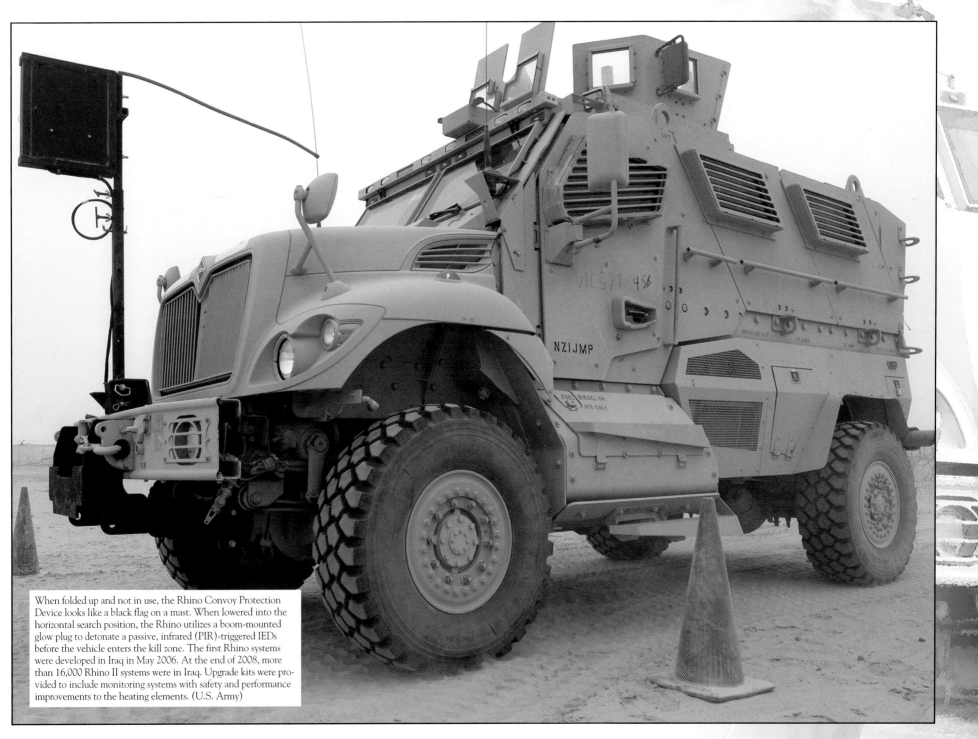

When folded up and not in use, the Rhino Convoy Protection Device looks like a black flag on a mast. When lowered into the horizontal search position, the Rhino utilizes a boom-mounted glow plug to detonate a passive, infrared (PIR)-triggered IEDs before the vehicle enters the kill zone. The first Rhino systems were developed in Iraq in May 2006. At the end of 2008, more than 16,000 Rhino II systems were in Iraq. Upgrade kits were provided to include monitoring systems with safety and performance improvements to the heating elements. (U.S. Army)

Top left: All-wheel mechanics assess the situation and begin the process of bolting and placing all the wires and parts of a new engine for a MaxxPro. (U.S. Army, Spc. Howard Alperin, MND-B PAO) **Above left:** An infantryman with Company C, 2nd Brigade, 2nd Battalion, 2nd Infantry Division opens the one-piece, tilting hood of one of the first MaxxPro vehicles to arrive in theater during a training course at Camp Liberty in western Baghdad. The Army soon learned, however, that the hood spring had a tendency to rub against the engine's air intake cooler when the hood was raised or lowered. If the problem remained untreated, crews would detect a whistling sound—the result of an air leak and loss of intake pressure. (U.S. Army Sgt. Mark B. Matthews) **Right:** The Michelin 395/85/R20 tires are equipped with run-flat inserts that allow the MaxxPro to travel about 18 miles at 30 mph (on hard, level service). After that, the run-flat inserts are prone to failure. (U.S. Navy, Mass Communication Specialist 1st Class (SW/AW) E. Rosario)

A U.S. Army soldier washes the windshield of a mine-resistant, ambush-protected (MRAP) vehicle at Forward Operating Base Gardez, Paktia province, Afghanistan. Soldiers performed weekly maintenance on their MRAPs to keep them combat ready. The rectangular antenna is part of the Counter-Radio controlled improvised explosive device Electronic Warfare (CREW) system. (U.S. Army, Sgt. Kimberly Trumbull)

A soldier works inside a MaxxPro Mine Resistant Ambush Protected vehicle to establish an upper tactical internet connection during a validation exercise. This photograph provides a good look at the interior two-piece black plastic trim, the upper and lower actuator on the edge of the door, as well as the locking devices. The chain and padlock hanging from the exterior grab handle are for externally locking the door. (U.S. Army, Lt. Col. Deanna Bague)

An Airman performs an acceptance limited technical inspection on an M1224 to ensure that all the systems and equipment on the vehicle are in working order before issuing it out to various units. There is a hydraulic system located in the rear of the vehicle which is part of the ramp. A dash-mounted toggle switch allows the driver to operate the ramp automatically. In the event of electrical failure, hydraulic failure, or for an emergency exit, the door can be lowered/raised using a manual release and a handle for the manual hydraulic pump. In a total failure, the ramp will free-fall. (U.S. Air Force, Senior Airman Julianne Showalter)

Top left: The vehicle's heating, ventilation, and air-conditioning (HVAC) system provides a comfortable cab environment by controlling temperature and humidity. It also features a special filtration system that protects the vehicle occupants from dust and chemical or biological contaminants. Regardless of these vehicle-provided comforts, an Army private tosses an empty box after loading sports drinks and water into a MaxxPro for an upcoming mission to escort convoys from Kuwait to Iraq. (U.S. Army, 1st Lt. Christian Venhuizen) **Top right:** An Army mechanic mans an M240B machine gun mounted in the Objective Gunner Protection Kit (O-GPK). Most U.S.-used MaxxPros were armed with either a 7.62mm M240B, the M2HB .50-caliber machine gun, or the Mk 19 Mod 3 automatic grenade launcher. (U.S.

Army, Major Myles Caggins) **Above left:** Members of the 594th Transportation Company prepare to inspect their new MaxxPros. The unit began using the MRAPs as part of their convoy escort teams moving supplies in and out of Iraq. Each one appears to be equipped with an AN/VAS-5 Driver's Vision Enhancer just above the space between the two windshield panels. (U.S. Army, Staff Sgt. William Watson Martin) **Above right:** Soldiers in an M1224 MaxxPro drive down a road while on patrol in Ghazni, Afghanistan, in 2010. The mast on the right rear is part of the CREW Duke vehicle-mounted electronic jammer designed to prevent remote detonation of land mines and IEDs. The two antennas on the cowl are for Single Channel Ground & Airborne Radios (SINCGARs). (U.S. Army, Sgt. Justin Howe)

Left: Despite driving aids like the Driver's Vision Enhancer device mounted on the roof, visibility from behind the steering wheel of the 10' tall MaxxPro is severely limited, often requiring outside guidance, such as this provided by a private of B Battery, 2nd Battalion, 300th Field Artillery, 115th Fires Brigade. (U.S. Army, 1st Lt. Christian Venhuizen) **Right:** U.S. soldiers with the 509th Infantry Regiment clean out the back of an M1224 at Forward Operating Base Gardez, Paktia province, Afghanistan, in 2012. Soldiers performed weekly maintenance on the MRAPs to keep them combat-ready. The antennae on the rear of the vehicle include a CREW Duke mast and a WIN-T Increment 2 system that provides the vehicle with voice and data communications without the need for a stationary command post. (U.S. Army, Sgt. Kimberly Trumbull)

A gunner mans his M2HB .50-caliber machine gun inside the O-GPK turret. Vehicle accessories visible include (left to right) SINCGARs antenna, CREW Duke electronic jammer antenna, and Driver's Vision Enhancer. The vehicle is equipped with a remote controlled spotlight mounted on the driver's side roof. The light is controlled by a wireless remote and/or a dash-mounted control that gives the operator a full 360-degree horizontal rotation and a 135-degree vertical tilt with fingertip control. (U.S. Army)

Afghan children stand aside as a M1224 MaxxPro passes through their village during a patrol in Khoshi District, Logar province, Afghanistan, in 2011. A naval mooring hawser is wound around the bumper to serve as a kinetic rope in towing operations. (U.S. Army, Spc. Andy Barrera)

Vehicles from Task Force Atlas, 141st Brigade Support Battalion, Oregon National Guard, 13th Sustainment Brigade (Expeditionary), are lined up ready to move out. Even though heavily equipped with an array of electronics, countermeasures, and additional LED lighting, these M1224s are the original vehicles Task Force Atlas received when they began their mission. Eventually, up-armored MRAPs replaced these trucks. (U.S. Army, Spc. Cory Grogan)

During a mission rehearsal exercise at Joint Multinational Readiness Center, Hohenfels, Germany, Georgian soldiers provide suppressing fire on the enemy while other soldiers medically evacuate their wounded buddies from Scout Platoon, Delta Co., 23rd Light Infantry Battalion after the platoon engaged in a firefight with enemy insurgents while on a reconnaissance mission. The black wires on the M1224 are part of the combat simulation gear. The bumper is marked "JMTC" to show it is assigned to the Center. (USMC, Gunnery Sgt. Alexis R. Mulero)

A generator mechanic assigned to the 1157th Transportation Company, Wisconsin National Guard, conducts preventive maintenance checks and services on an M1224 before a mission at Bagram Air Field, Afghanistan. The headlights on this particular vehicle have been replaced with LED units and extra LED lights are mounted on the front bumper. The UHG SATCOM "eggbeater" antenna above the driver's position allows SATCOM-on-the-move (SOTM) operations. It can be used with most tactical multi-band, multi-mode receivers. (U.S. Army)

MRAP recovery is dangerous, not only because of the combat environment and difficult terrain, but because of the approximately 43,500 pound weight and the high center of gravity. If the towing vehicle is of the same or heavier weight, a Marine Corps MTVR tow bar is usually used. A HEMMT wrecker, as seen here, can use chains and its lift tube to front-tow a MaxxPro. (U.S. Army, Spc. Candace Foster)

The Self-Protection Adaptive Roller Kit (SPARK) was a modular mine roller system designed to be mounted on tactical wheeled platforms. The front roller consisted of 2 roller banks on the left and right side of the vehicle, providing contact with the ground, causing IEDs to detonate on the roller. This forces as much of the blast down and away from the vehicle as possible, as opposed to underneath the vehicle. (U.S. Army, Sgt Belynda Faulkner)

Deployment of new or upgraded models of MaxxPros did not mean old versions were taken off the front line. In fact, the older vehicles continued in service with U.S. troops or coalition forces, often with field-applied countermeasures, like this Model 1224 used by the Romanian 280th Mechanized Infantry Battalion photographed in Afghanistan in 2012. (U.S. Army, Lt. Col. Daniel Bohmer)

M1224A1

On 31 July 2007, the U.S. Marine Corps issued a request for proposal for the MRAP II Enhanced Vehicle Competition. The MRAP II was intended to defeat Explosively-Formed Penetrators (EFPs). These stand-off improvised explosive devices employed a shaped charge against the sides of vehicles. Because existing MRAPs would also be required to address this threat, the Marines initiated the MRAP Expedient Armor Program (MEAP). Basically, MEAP was an appliqué armor kit that could be retrofitted to existing MRAPs. Whether retrofitted or produced MEAP-ready, the new version of the MaxxPro was designated the M1224A1. The vehicle on the left is an M1224A1, whereas the vehicle on the right is an M1234 MaxxPro Plus. Both types of vehicles were in service with Delta Troop, 5th Squadron, 4th Cavalry Regiment, 2nd Brigade, 1st Infantry Division in 2008. (U.S. Air Force, Senior Airman Daniel Owen)

M1224A1 MaxxPro Specifications	
Type	Category I MRAP
Length	254 inches
Width	102 inches
Height	120 inches
Minimum ground clearance	10.9 inches
GVWR	48,000 lbs.
Kit weight	4,500 lbs.
Engine	MaxxForce D8.7 Diesel
Horsepower	330 @ 2,100 rpm
Minimum turning distance (curb to curb)	62 feet
Maximum slope	30% side / 50% long grade
Center of gravity (GVW vertical)	61 inches
Center of gravity (GVW vertical)	59.4 inches

Top left: One of the components of the expedient armor required specialty steel that was processed into add-on armor. These material designs, commonly referred to as P900 or XPA, were made at only a few foundries. The U.S. military accepted 550 MEAP-ready vehicles: 50 retrofitted with boss-style attachments, and 500 vehicles made MEAP-ready before shipping from the manufacturer. In this image, a MEAP-equipped vehicle in the lead is also fitted with an improvised overhead wire mitigation apparatus and an AN/VAS-5A Driver Vision Enhancer. (U.S. Army) **Top right:** In addition to the MEAP add-on armor, additional protective measures on this M1224A1 used by the 328th Brigade Support Battalion, 56th Stryker Brigade Combat Team, includes a wire mesh deflector to protect against hand-thrown explosives, overhead wire mitigation kit, and a Rhino system convoy protection device. (U.S. Army, Sgt. Doug Roles) **Above left:** Members of the 328th Brigade Support Battalion, 56th Stryker Brigade Combat Team, place HESCO-produced wire mesh on a metal outrigger attached to the MEAP mounts on their M1224A1. (U.S. Army, Sgt. Doug Roles)

M1234

Whereas the extra armor rendered MEAP-equipped MaxxPros less susceptible to EFP attacks, it also made them too heavy for the MaxxForce D8.7-liter engine and the suspension. In 2008, the manufacturer, now known as Navistar Defense, introduced an upgraded vehicle capable of carrying increased EFP protection: the M1234 MaxxPro Plus. The new Category I MRAP was designed to accept the Frag Kit 6 armor package in addition to featuring enhanced performance with an increased load-carrying dual rear wheels and a 375-horsepower D9.3I6 MaxxForce D engine. Identifying characteristics of the M1234 are dual rear wheels, with horizontal grille slats, rectangular grille on the air conditioning unit on the right side of the vehicle, and no protective rims around the door handles. (U.S. Army)

M1234 MaxxPro Plus Specifications	
Type	Category I MRAP
Length	254 inches
Width	102 inches
Height	120 inches
Minimum ground clearance	10.9 inches
GVWR	53,000 lbs.
Engine	MaxxForce D9.3 Diesel
Horsepower	375 @ 2,200 rpm
Minimum turning distance (curb to curb)	62 feet
Maximum slope	30% side / 60% long grade
Center of gravity (GVW vertical)	61 inches

Top left: M1234s equipped with full EFP-defeating armor packages and M-ATVs offloaded at Pier 8 in the port city of Busan, Republic of Korea. Previously used in Iraq, they were relocated to the Korean Peninsula in 2012. (U.S. Army, Staff Sgt. Robert DeDeaux) **Right:** An NCO and a specialist review inventory sheets of their newly received M1234 at the Camp Liberty MRAP fielding site in 2008. The A-Kit mounting bracket for the EFP armor package is visible just over the sergeant's shoulder. (US Army, Sgt. Daniel Blottenberger)

Despite adding about 8,000 lbs and 18 inches to the M1234's operational weight and width, a fully EFP-defeating armor-equipped MaxxPro was air-transportable. This particular truck rolled off a C-5 Galaxy at Osan Air Force Base, Republic of Korea in July 2012. (U.S. Air Force, Tech. Sgt. Eric Petosky)

Each of the M1234s delivered by the 370th Trans. Co., 275th Combat Sustainment Support Battalion, 77th Sustainment Brigade in 2011 appears to be equipped the same—with full armor protection against EFPs, O-GPK turret, additional roof-mounted spotlight, FBCB2 Blue Force Tracking antenna above the driver, CREW Duke electronic jammer antenna on the back, and bumper-mounted Rhino bracket. (U.S. Army, Spc. Matthew G. Keeler)

A fully equipped M1234 of the 3rd Sustainment Brigade moves out on a convoy escort mission in 2011. In addition to the new engine, the M1234 received an increased capacity drive train, dual steering gear, and a 570-amp alternator. When fully loaded with armor, crew, and combat gear, the 43,000+ pound vehicle could still hit a top speed of 69.2 miles per hour. (U.S. Army)

An M1234 rolls past members of the 3rd Brigade Combat Team, "GREYWOLF", 1st Cavalry Division (3/1 CD); the last unit out of Iraq. The photo shows the extent to which the MaxxPro had evolved during service in Iraq, resplendent with EFP-defeating armor, O-GPK turret, Rhino Convoy Protection Device, multiple LED spotlights, CREW system, and Blue Force tracker. (U.S. Army, Staff Sgt. Lynette R. Hoke)

This pair of M1234s was part of the protective services detail of the 1073rd Maintenance Company, 2nd Squadron, 278th Armored Cavalry Regiment, 13th Sustainment Command (Expeditionary). Their primary task was to drive for VIPs who required ground transport from base to base. (U.S. Army, SPC Chad Menegay)

A two-soldier team of driver and truck commander with the 370th Trans. Co. un-load their armor-upgraded M1234 off the back of the HET trailer on Contingency Operating Base Warhorse, Iraq. The U.S. Army Research Laboratory designed The Frag Kit 6 kit to defeat EFPs. It adds about 12" width to each side of the vehicle. (U.S. Army, Specialist Matthew G. Keeler)

An 82nd Airborne trooper rests on the ramp of a MaxxPro Plus shortly after crossing the border to Kuwait on Dec. 9, 2011. (U.S. Army, Staff Sgt. Lynette R. Hoke)

After leaving their base in Iraq for the final time and traveling to Kuwait, an 82nd Airborne gunner hangs a flag from the overhead wire mitigation kit on his M1234 at Khabari Crossing. An L-Rod-covered Buffalo is directly behind the MaxxPro. (U.S. Army, Staff Sgt. Lynette R. Hoke)

U.S. Airmen with the 455th Air Expeditionary Wing, Task Force Reaper, set up a traffic check point north of Bagram Air Field, June 6, 2012. A specially created version of the M1234 was delivered to the Air Force, differing only in internal arrangement and communication packages. Externally, there was no difference from the standard M1234. (U.S. Army, Sgt. Ken Scar)

In addition to the M1234, an ambulance version—M1234A1—was deployed to Iraq. The ambulance was designed with the same basic V-shaped hull on the crew capsule but the interior was equipped to administer to two litter patients and walking wounded. All M1234A1 ambulances in Iraq were equipped with Frag 6 armor kits. (U.S. Army)

A gunner from the 5th Infantry Regiment, 3rd Infantry Brigade Combat Team, 1st Armored Division maintains vigilance from his O-GPK-turreted M1234 MaxxPro Plus. Bosses for attaching external armor are visible on the driver's door. (U.S. Army, Sgt. Gustavo Olgiati)

A wheeled vehicle driver with the 396th Transportation Company, 157th Combat Sustainment Support Battalion, Task Force Durable stands in front of his recently delivered M1234 at Bagram Airfield in Parwan province, Afghanistan. When M1234s were redeployed from Iraq to Afghanistan, it was found that EFPs were not as great a concern, so Frag-6 armor was generally removed. In its place, though, troops hung screens of rocket propelled grenade (RPG) defeating netting. (U.S. Army, Sgt. V. Michelle Woods)

U.S. soldiers with 1st Battalion, 5th Cavalry Regiment pull mounted security at an entry control point to the U.S. Consulate Herat, Herat province, Afghanistan, inside an M1234 that still retains the mounting brackets for the Frag-6 armor. (U.S. Army, Spc. Ryan D. Green)

M1235

On 4 September 2008, the U.S. Marine Corps awarded Navistar a $752 million contract to produce a lighter, smaller, and more mobile MaxxPro variant that would be able to navigate the rough terrain encountered in Afghanistan. Production began the following month. By February 2009, more than 800 MaxxPro "Dash" vehicles had been delivered. These Dash vehicles belonging to the 4th Battalion, 25th Field Artillery Regiment, 3rd Brigade Combat Team, 10th Mountain Division are covered with snow while parked at a motor pool inside Forward Operation Base Airborne, Afghanistan—a condition never encountered by their larger MaxxPro brethren in Iraq! (U.S. Army, Sgt. Teddy Wade)

M1235 MaxxPro Dash Specifications	
Length	246 inches
Width	102 inches
Height	109 inches
Minimum ground clearance	10.9 inches
GVWR	49,000 lbs.
Engine	MaxxForce D9.3 Diesel
Horsepower	375 @ 2,200 rpm
Minimum turning distance (curb to curb)	54 feet
Maximum slope	30% side / 60% long grade
Center of gravity (GVW vertical)	57.6 inches

M1235A1 MaxxPro Dash DXM Specifications	
Length	246 inches
Width	103.4 inches
Height	115 inches
Minimum ground clearance	15.5 inches
GVWR	51,500 lbs.
Engine	MaxxForce D9.3 Diesel
Horsepower	375 @ 2,200 rpm
Minimum turning distance (curb to curb)	54 feet
Maximum slope	30% side / 60% long grade
Center of gravity (GVW vertical)	57.6 inches

Top left: The M1235 Dash's identifying characteristics include horizontal grille slats, a shorter protected passenger compartment, rectangular vents below the passenger compartment, a recessed area above the vent and storage box that reveals the compartment's V-shape, and single rear tires. (U.S. Army) **Above left:** Paratroopers and a MaxxPro Dash from 2nd Battalion, 377th Parachute Field Artillery Regiment, 4th Brigade Combat Team, 25th Infantry Division secure a helicopter landing zone, overlooking parts of the city of Khost in eastern Afghanistan. The Dash is equipped with an Army heavy-duty tow bar lashed to the front bumper, and a spine board used for casualty removal. (U.S. Army, Staff Sgt. Marcus Butler)

Lighter and with more maneuverability than the M1234 MaxxPro Plus, the Dash was designed to support small-unit combat operations in either urban or confined areas in addition to usual missions such as convoy operations, troop transport, or reconnaissance. Here, a Marine with Company E, 2nd Battalion, 8th Marine Regiment loads improvised explosive device-making materials found in a nearby compound into an M1235. Bosses for attaching additional armor are visible on the driver's door and the first two Plasan armor panels of the passenger compartment. (U.S. Marine Corps, 1st Lt. Kurt Stahl)

Weekly maintenance keeps the MRAPs combat ready. U.S. soldiers with the 3rd Battalion (Airborne), 509th Infantry Regiment, Task Force 4-25 check a leak on an M1235A1 Dash at Forward Operating Base Gardez, Paktia province, Afghanistan, The Dash rolls on Michelin 395/85R20 XZL tires with Hutchinson Runflats. (U.S. Army, Sgt. Kimberly Trumbull)

A U.S. Army Specialist from 3rd Battalion (Airborne), 509th Infantry Regiment, Task Force 4-25 checks the fluid levels of a MaxxPro Dash at Forward Operating Base Gardez, Paktia province, Afghanistan. The MaxxForce four-stroke D9.3 6-cylinder features turbo inter-cooling and direct electronic injection. It uses a low-pressure fuel supply pump. It has a generation-two electro-hydraulic fuel system that includes an under-valve-cover oil manifold, fuel injectors, and a high-pressure oil pump. Additional engine strength comes from the crankcase and bearing ladder cap, whereas the single-piece steel pistons and six head bolts per cylinder promote a longer engine life. (U.S. Army, Sgt. Kimberly Trumbull)

A U.S. Army corporal of 3rd Battalion (Airborne), 509th Infantry Regiment, Task Force 4-25 washes the windows of a MaxxPro Dash at Forward Operating Base Gardez, Paktia province, Afghanistan. Like the doors on the M1234 Plus, the doors on the Dash do not have a rim around the handle. (U.S. Army, Sgt. Kimberly Trumbull)

Soldiers of the 5th Brigade, 2nd Infantry Division Stryker Brigade Combat Team equip their XM153 Common Remotely Operated Weapon Station (CROWS) II with an M2 .50-caliber machine gun as they familiarize themselves with the new weapon system during their training. The CROWS is a three-axis, stabilized mount that contains a sensor suite and fire control software, allowing on-the-move target acquisition. (U.S. Army, Sgt. Elisebet Freeburg)

U.S. Army soldiers assigned to 3rd Battalion (Airborne), 509th Infantry Regiment, Task Force 4-25 complete a list of checks to perform on a MaxxPro Dash fitted with frames of netting suspending metal nodes. Navistar delivered more than 2,300 RPG Net Kits to troops in the field to install. The netting has proved to be especially effective in defeating rocket propelled grenades (RPGs). (U.S. Army, Sgt. Kimberly Trumbull)

The Dash has a new, one-piece air conditioner housing with a rectangular grille behind the passenger side door. (U.S. Army)

A U.S. Army Chief Warrant Officer 2, who is also an AH-64 Apache pilot serving as a brigade aviation element officer with the 82nd Airborne Division's 1st Brigade Combat Team, unpacks a Puma unmanned aerial vehicle from the side of a Dash. (U.S. Army, Sgt. Michael J. MacLeod)

A U.S. Army MaxxPro Dash armed with a CROWS II turret provides security while coalition soldiers blow up an improvised explosive device 300 meters away in Jalrez, Afghanistan. (U.S. Army, Sgt. Teddy Wade)

U.S. Air Force Airmen assigned to the 455th Expeditionary Aircraft Maintenance Unit explore a MaxxPro Dash during an equipment familiarization meeting with U.S. Marines assigned to Georgian Deployment Program - International Security Assistance Force Rotation 14 on the flight line at Bagram Air Field, Afghanistan. The RPG-defeating netting frames are mounted to the vehicle with a special set of brackets that hold the assembly about 20 inches from the body of the vehicle, which allows for normal equipment stowage behind the net. (U.S. Air Force, Staff Sgt. Whitney Amstutz)

Navistar upgraded the ramp system on the M1235 and M1235A1 (seen here) to allow it to be lowered or raised in just six seconds. (Army National Guard, Sgt. 1st Class Jim Downen Jr.)

Like the base model MaxxPro and the Plus, the Dash had a turret ring that accepts systems like the O-GPK (seen here) or CROWS turret. (U.S. Air Force photo, Staff Sgt. Brian Ferguson)

The Dash's center of gravity dropped to 57.6" as compared to 59.4" for the M1224 base model MaxxPro and the M1234 Plus. The bracket on the front bumper is for installing the SPARK mine roller. (Arthur Macon)

In addition to a MaxxPro DASH equipped with a full RPG-defeating netting suite, vehicles staged nearby a section of the Khowst-Gardez Road that was washed out due to heavy rains in Khowst Province, Afghanistan include M983A4 HEMTT tractors and trailers, an M-ATV (center right, rear), and an RG-31A2 with full L-rod suite (left). (U.S. Army, Sgt. Joshua B. Dwyer)

A U.S. Air Force Airman with the 455th Expeditionary Logistics Readiness Squadron pressure washes an M1234 Plus at Bagram Airfield, Afghanistan in 2012. Though more stable MRAP platforms like the M1235 Dash or the Oshkosh-produced M-ATV had been widely distributed throughout Afghanistan by this time, less nimble MRAPs (like this M1234) were shipped to Afghanistan to perform primarily road duties like airfield patrol, convoy protection, or VIP escort. Though this is a late-production M1234 (as evidenced by the rectangular vent covering behind the driver's door), the tell-tale that this is a Plus are the dual rear wheels and the extension off the rear of the crew compartment. (U.S. Air Force, Senior Airman Kayla Newman)

A Dash equipped with a SPARK mine roller and RPG-defeating netting prepares for a route clearing patrol mission after heavy snowfall in Parwan Province, Afghanistan. Apparently, the gunner has yet to discover that the O-GPK turret is filled with snow! (U.S. Army, 1st Lt. Henry Chan)

The Self-Protection Adaptive Roller Kit System II (SPARKS II) attached to the front of a DASH DXM detonates roadside bombs before they have a chance to harm service members riding in the cab. This is the same as other mine rollers, but SPARKS II allows the driver to make on-the-spot changes from inside the vehicle affecting how the roller operates, rather than getting out and making manual adjustments to the roller. (U.S. Army, Sgt. Ken Scar)

On 16 February 2010, the U.S. Marine Corps Systems Command. Awarded a $752 million contract for 1,050 MaxxPro Dash vehicles to Navistar. The vehicles supplied under the contract included the DXM independent suspension solution provided by Hendrickson Truck Suspension Systems and AxleTech International. The new upgrade increases the vehicle's off-road capabilities, necessary for operations in Afghanistan. The new suspension was so successful, Navistar was contracted to upgrade 2,717 older MaxxPros of all variants. (U.S. Army, Spc. Austin Berner)

U.S. Air Force Airmen assigned to the 455th Expeditionary Aircraft Maintenance Unit and U.S. Marines operating a Dash DXM and assigned to Georgian Deployment Program - International Security Assistance Force Rotation pose for a photo following an equipment familiarization meeting at Bagram Air Field, Afghanistan. Because Airmen operating the EC-130 Hercules provide support to Marines during outside the wire missions, the meeting afforded an opportunity for both groups to become better acquainted with equipment and procedures utilized during joint missions. (U.S. Air Force, Staff Sgt. Whitney Amstutz)

Soldiers assigned to the 3rd Squadron "Thunder," 3rd Cavalry Regiment conduct mounted and dismounted patrols at the National Training Center, as part of Security Force Assistance Brigade Rotation in 2014. The two Dash DXMs flank an M-ATV. (U.S. Army, Sgt. 1st Class Alan B. Owens)

Commonly referred to as "ISS," the Hendrickson-supplied sub frames, sway bars, coil springs and shocks combined with the Axle Tech 500 series Independent Suspension Axle System makes the M1235A1 Dash DXM about six inches taller than the standard M1235 Dash. Besides the slightly increased height, the remote central tire inflation system (CTIS) and downward opening curve of the lower suspension are tell-tale signs of a DXM model (also referred to as the "Dash ISS"). (U.S. Army, Sgt. Michael J. MacLeod)

A gunner with the 82nd Airborne Division's 1st Brigade Combat Team removes his M240B machine gun from its CROWS II mount after his M1235A1 (parked between two M-ATVs) returned from a combat logistics patrol in Ghazni Province, Afghanistan. (U.S. Army, by Sgt. Michael J. MacLeod)

The characteristic coiled springs and curved lower suspension immediately identifies this Dash patrolling Afghanistan's Highway 1 in Ghazni province as a DXM model. In addition to its usual combat roles, Navistar adapted the DASH DXM as an ambulance when the company received an order for 250 in May 2011. Designated the M1235A2, the Dash DXM Ambulance was designed to carry a driver and two crew, one of whom is a medic, in addition to a combination of two litter-bound or four ambulatory patients. (U.S. Army, Sgt. Michael J. MacLeod)

Soldiers with the 3rd Battalion (Airborne), 509th Infantry Regiment, Task Force 4-25 close the hood of an M1235A1 at Forward Operating Base Gardez, Paktia province, Afghanistan. The weekly maintenance requires checking the fluid levels, wiring, and hoses of the MaxxForce D9.3 engine. Used in both the Dash and the Dash DXM, the engine is coupled to an Allison 3200 SP/5-speed automatic transmission. The heavy-duty tow bar is secured to the top of the SPARK mounting bracket. (U.S. Army, Sgt. Kimberly Trumbull)

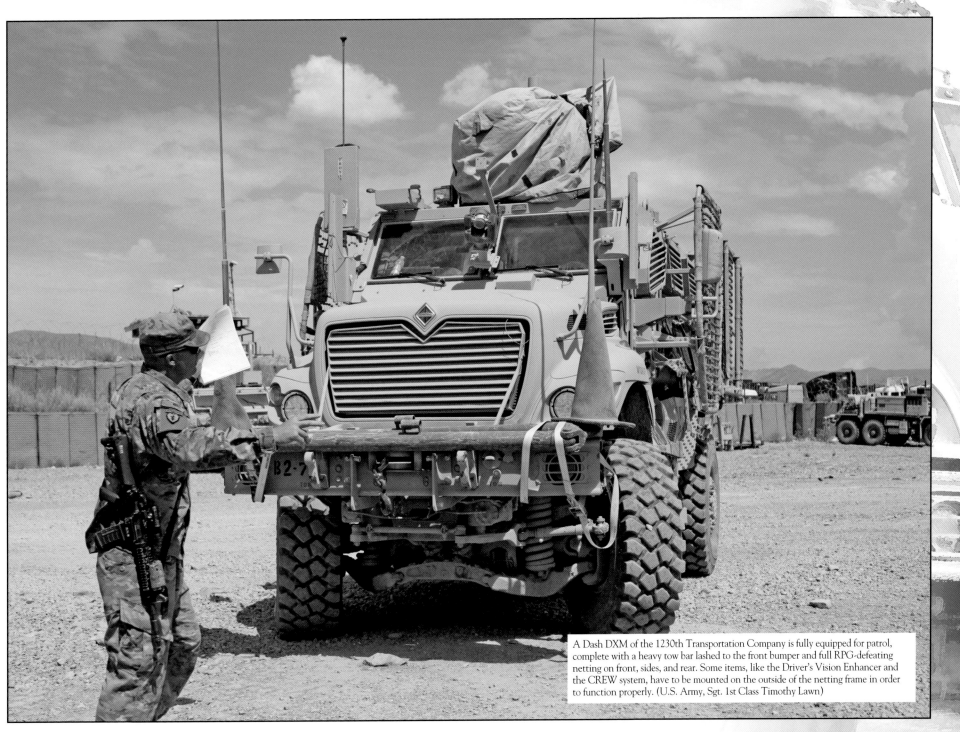

A Dash DXM of the 1230th Transportation Company is fully equipped for patrol, complete with a heavy tow bar lashed to the front bumper and full RPG-defeating netting on front, sides, and rear. Some items, like the Driver's Vision Enhancer and the CREW system, have to be mounted on the outside of the netting frame in order to function properly. (U.S. Army, Sgt. 1st Class Timothy Lawn)

Soldiers of the 1230th Transportation Company practiced the Mine Resistant Ambush Protected Vehicle, Hasty Hook-Up drills with a pair of Dash DXMs. The photo gives a good view of the double-bar system used for mounting the RPG-defeating nets as well as showing how far they extend beyond the end of the vehicle. (U.S. Army, Sgt. 1st Class Timothy Lawn)

M1235A1 Dash DXMs and M-ATVs sit on Forward Operating Base Tagab, Kapisa province, Afghanistan. The Dashes are equipped with heavy tow bars attached to the front tow hooks. A casualty litter is lashed to the outside of the RPG Protection Kit on the Dash in the foreground. (U.S. Army, Spc. Andrew Claire Baker)

Paratroopers with the 82nd Airborne Division's 1st Brigade Combat Team return from a patrol in Afghanistan's southern Ghazni province. The Dash DXM with the ramp down has a SATCOM antenna mounted on the right rear corner. The trooper standing on top of an L-Rod-equipped RG-31A2 is adjusting the vehicle's Gyrocam. (U.S. Army, Sgt. Michael J. MacLeod)

Troopers from the 82nd Airborne Division's 1st Brigade Combat Team prepare an M1235A1 for a resupply mission at Forward Operating Base Arian, Ghazni Province, Afghanistan. The vehicle is sufficiently prepared for a night operation, having four LED lights mounted on the crew compartment, one off the corner of the windshield, and additional lighting on the front bumper and corner of the mine roller. (U.S. Army, Sgt. Michael J. MacLeod)

Difficulty of driving a SPARKS II at night is minimized by sufficient light provided by LED lights on the front of the roller and top of the windshield netting frame. (U.S. Army, Sgt. 1st Class Timothy Lawn)

Puffs of black Diesel fuel smoke pour out of a CROWS-equipped M1235A1 as it pushes the SPARKS II roller over open ground. The stronger engine, tighter turn radius, and lower center of gravity made the M1235A1 one of the most useful MRAPs deployed to Afghanistan. In 2013, Dash DXMs in Afghanistan received the MaxxPro Survivability Upgrade (MSU). Re-designated as M1235A3s, each of the upgraded trucks received improved front and rear Jankel seats with front seat towers and rear seat brackets, a transmission retention bracket, welded seams on both exterior and interior of the cab, front and rear Skydex Blast Mats, Crew Ripple Floors, seam plates, rear wall retention brackets, and upgraded rear suspension springs. (U.S. Army, Sgt. Michael J. MacLeod)

M1249 MRV

Growing out of the MaxxPro program, the all-wheel drive MRAP Recovery Vehicle (MRV) provides extraordinary towing, lifting, and recovery capabilities from an MRAP-level protected platform, allowing heavy battlefield asset recovery under combat conditions. It is delivered with complete sets of special tools, training, and spare parts. The MRV pictured lifting concrete barriers into place wears Q-Net protection over the cab area. It was assigned to the 4th Infantry Brigade Combat Team, 3rd Infantry Division. (U.S. Army, Sgt. Sarah Bailey)

M1249 MaxxPro MRAP Recovery Vehicle (MRV) Specifications	
Length	407.9 inches
Width	102 inches
Height	117 inches
Minimum ground clearance	10.9 inches
GVWR	81,000 lbs.
Engine	MaxxForce D9.3 Diesel
Horsepower	375 @ 2,200 rpm
Minimum turning distance (curb to curb)	94 feet

Top left: Unveiled in February 2009, the MaxxPro MRAP Recovery Vehicle (MRV) promised to deliver an MRAP-level protection platform capable of recovering other vehicles that have been damaged by IEDs. The company received an order for 250 MRVs in November 2010. Designated the M1249, this is one of the MRVs debuted at Bagram Air Field. (U.S. Army, Sgt. Scott Davis) **Top right:** The MRV is capable of recovering all Category I (like the RG-31A2) and II MRAP vehicles as well as all forms of the Stryker vehicle. It can tow up to 81,000 pounds. (U.S. Army, Staff Sgt. Peter Weidenbacher) **Above left:** The MRV allows two- to three-man crews to retrieve damaged or mission-disabled vehicles and carry out other support missions. The vehicle provides its crew with the same ballistics, mine and IED protection used on all MaxxPro MRAP vehicles. This particular truck is fitted with some of the same combat-essential gear used on other MRAPs, including the RPG-defeating netting, Driver's Vision Enhancer and CREW/Duke anti-IED system. (U.S. Navy, Mass Communication Specialist 2nd Class Jon Rasmussen)

The M1249 doesn't have any armament in the basic configuration. A DXM independent suspension and central tire inflation system is fitted to the front wheels. A six-channel anti-lock brake system contributes to improved traction, especially in soft terrain. (John Lewis)

The M1249 uses the V-shape hull design coupled with armor. Like other MaxxPro family vehicles, the MRV provides troops with an increased level of protection against small arms fire, RPGs, mine blasts, and IEDs. An auxiliary fuel tank provides the vehicle with an extended range. (John Lewis)

The M1249 uses many of the some of the same parts used to build MaxxPro MRAPs such as an Allison transmission, 570-amp alternator, and 375-horsepower engine. The MRV uses a 6x6 chassis: two wheels at the front, and four sets of dual wheels at the rear. (John Lewis)

MAX LOAD CAP 60000 LBS
LOAD TEST 05/2012
NEXT TEST 05-2013

A recovery crane is mounted on the rear of the chassis with tool boxes on the right and left sides. Additional recovery power is available through an additional winch mounted on the front of the vehicle. (John Lewis)

The MRV is just the latest of nearly 9,000 MaxxPro MRAP vehicles to have safely conveyed convoys, made route clearances, and provided troop protection in Iraq and Afghanistan. Here, an M1249 MRV belonging to Clearance Patrol-29, Alpha Company, 4th Brigade Special Troops Battalion, 4th Infantry Brigade leads yet another safe return of a convoy that had made a nonstop mission to clear the route of IEDs. (U.S. Army, Staff Sgt. Zach Holden)